HAND SHADOWS

TO BE THROWN UPON THE WALL:

CAMEL.

Hy Burvill Invt Et Delt

HAND SHADOWS

TO BE THROWN UPON THE WALL:

A SERIES OF NOVEL AND AMUSING FIGURES FORMED BY THE HAND.

FROM

ORIGINAL DESIGNS

BY

HENRY BURSILL.

—•—

Second Edition.

—•—

LONDON:

GRIFFITH AND FARRAN,

(SUCCESSORS TO NEWBERY AND HARRIS),

CORNER OF ST. PAUL'S CHURCHYARD.

—

M.DCCC.LIX.

MEMBER OF
INDEPENDENT PUBLISHERS GUILD

© 1993 PRYOR PUBLICATIONS
75 Dargate Road, Yorkletts, Whitstable,
Kent CT5 3AE, England.
Tel. & Fax: (0227) 274655
Specialist in Facsimile Reproductions.

Reprinted 1997

A CIP Record for this book is available from the British Library

ISBN 0 946014 248

Pryor Publications wish to thank
Peter Stockham for his advice and assistance
in the publication of this book.

Printed and bound by
Whitstable Litho Printers Ltd., Whitstable.

PREFACE.

———◆———

I NEED not explain how these Shadows were suggested, to any one who has seen WILKIE'S picture, " The Rabbit on the Wall." But by what pains they were invented can never be revealed ; for it is known to my tortured digits alone, and they, luckily for me, are dumb. I calculate that I put my ten fingers through hundreds of various exercises before my " Bird " took wing ; my left little finger thrills at the memory of " Grandpapa." Yet *now* how easy it is to make the " Duck " to quack, the " Donkey " to bray, " Toby " to wag his tail, and the " Rabbit " to munch his unsubstantial meal.

Of course the Shadows are not to be reproduced perfectly, on " one trial only " ; but I believe that in each case I have drawn the due position of the fingers with such care, that the most difficult subject may be accomplished after a few minutes ; nor need ingenious youth or parental fondness confine their endeavours to the sketches contained in this book. With a little ingenuity and some patience, new shadows may be produced ; and not unfrequently figures appear that one never dreamed of attempting.

Other Books of Shadows have been published ; but it will be seen at a glance that mine bears affinity to none. Some of my sketches were made years ago, others when a student at the Academy. Indeed, the Shadows have often been displayed on the walls of my studio, much to the amusement of fellow-students, who would, I am sure, at any time bear witness to their originality.

HENRY BURSILL.

December, 1858.

THE GOOSE A PRISONER.

Hy Burvill Inv. Et Del.

DEER.

Hy. Burvill Invt. Et Delt.

GRANDPAPA.

Hᵧ Burvill Inᵗ Et Delᵗ

BUNNY.

Wᵐ Burvill Inᵗ Et Delᵗ

A BIRD IN FLIGHT.

Hy Burvill Invt Et Delt

GOAT.

H. Burvill Invt. Et Delt.

DOG TOBY.

Hy Bursill Invt Et Delt

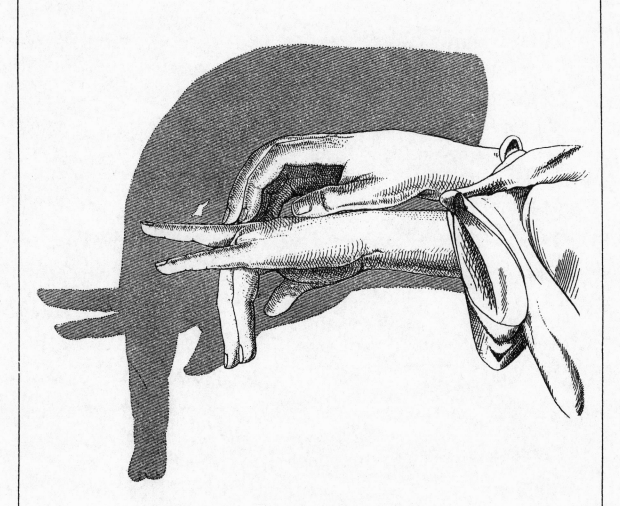

AN ELEPHANT.

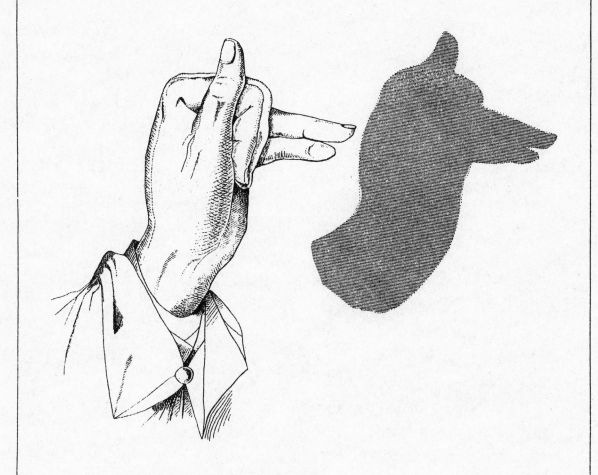

GREYHOUND.

Wᵐ Bursill Inᵗ Et Delᵗ

PIG.

Hy Bursill Inv.t Et Del.t

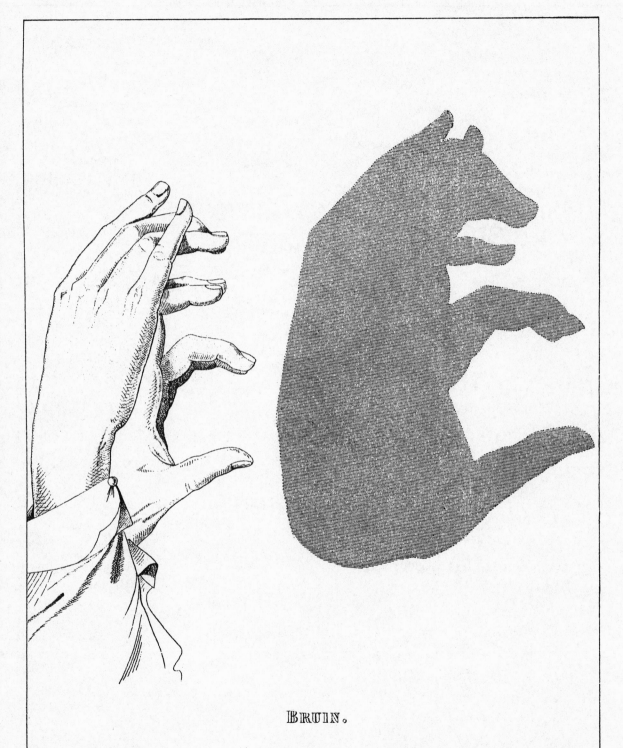

BRUIN.

Wm Bursill Inv.^t Et Del.^t

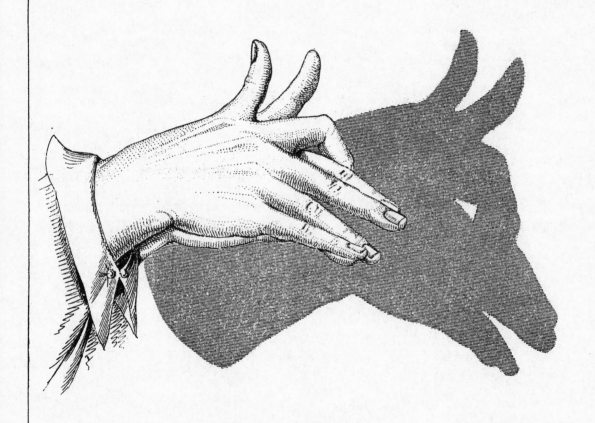

A PORTRAIT.

Hy Burvill Invt Et Delt

OLD GROWLER.

Hy Bursill Invt Et Delt

FRIGHT.

Wm Burvill Invt Et Delt

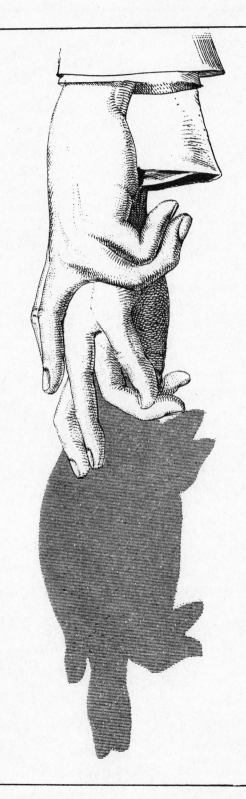

A TORTOISE.

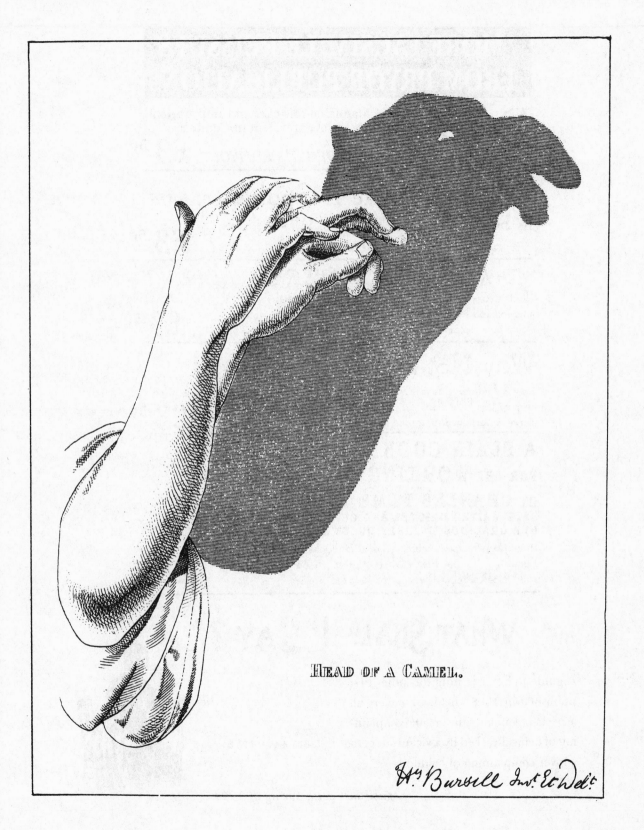

HEAD OF A CAMEL.

Wᵐ Burvell Invᵗ Et Delᵗ

OUR NATIVE ENGLAND,

BEING THE
HISTORY OF ENGLAND MADE EASY

A brief description of each ruler through
the ages; with 47 woodcuts.

£2.^{.99} £2.⁹⁹

LABOUR-SAVING HINTS AND IDEAS FOR THE HOME

Contains over 1,300 hints and ideas for the home, selected
from over 30,000 entries that were submitted to a
competition run in the early 1920s.

£7.⁹⁹

Old London Cries

"Buy a fine Singing Bird?"

This hard back book is hand bound with marbled paper
and unusual book ties; it also has a hand coloured
frontispiece.

A quality reprint of an 1885 edition with over 140 pages
of informative and interesting reading, together with
over 50 woodcuts depicting various street traders of
London from the seventeenth century.

"Beautifully illustrated"—*London's City Recorder*

Price

£7.95

CHILDREN'S SINGING GAMES

SECOND SERIES

1894

DAVID NUTT IN THE STRAND

A SECOND SERIES OF CHILDREN'S SINGING GAMES WILL BE PUBLISHED
IN AUGUST 1993 IN THE SAME FORMAT AS THE SERIES IT CONTAINS.

London Bridge is Broken Down	Round and Round the Village
Sally Water	The Jolly Miller
Three Sailors	Oats and Beans and Barley
Looby Loo	Here we Come up the Green Grass

With more superb illustrations by Winifred Smith, this book is a further
celebration of the work of Alice Gomme.

Size 235mm x 226mm Landscape
74 Pages Hardback

ISBN 0946014 13 2

Price **£7**.⁹⁹

This facsimile of *"Nursery Songs and Rhymes of England Pictured in Black and White,"* first published in 1895, will have wide appeal. There are 25 nursery songs and rhymes in all, with superb illustrations by Winifred Smith, some of her finest work. This is a book that has long needed to be re-published, equally as part of our heritage as for the book's charm and simplicity.

Size 227mm x 250mm
66 Pages Hardback

ISBN 094 6014 14 0

Price **£7.**99

A full list of our publications sent free on request.

MANNERS for MEN

By Mrs Humphry
"Madge" of "Truth"

LIKE every other woman, I have my ideal of manhood. The difficulty is to describe it. First of all, he must be a gentleman; but that means so much that it, in its turn, requires explanation . . .

Price

£4.50

Size 20cm x 10cm
176 Pages Paperback
ISBN 0 946014 23 X

MANNERS for WOMEN

By Mrs Humphry
"Madge" of "Truth"
author of
"MANNERS for MEN"

"A useful reminder that tittering is an unpleasant habit and that courtsying should be avoided unless you know what you are doing.

FIRST PUBLISHED 1897; OWING TO "
DEMAND IS BEING REPUBLISHED.

—THE TIMES, *July 1993*

Price

£3.95

Size 20cm x 10cm
164 Pages Paperback
ISBN 0 946014 175

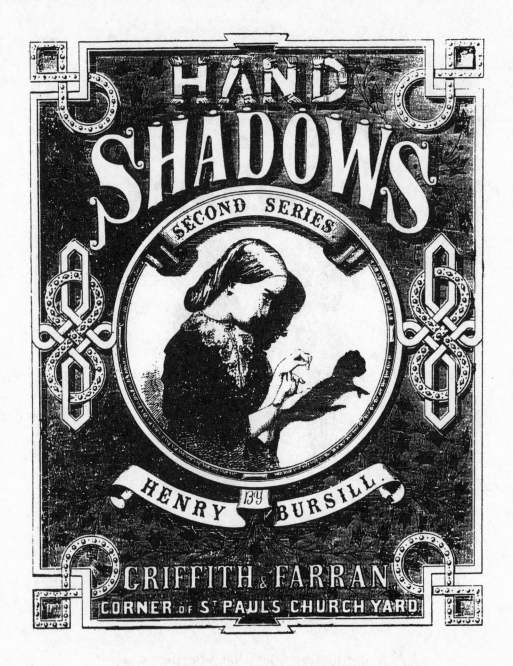

HAND SHADOWS

SECOND SERIES

BY HENRY BURSILL

GRIFFITH & FARRAN
CORNER OF St PAULS CHURCH YARD

*A second volume of Hand Shadows will be
published in the spring of 1994.*

Available from bookshops or post free from
PRYOR PUBLICATIONS

75 Dargate Road, Yorkletts, Whitstable, Kent CT5 3AE, England.
Tel. & Fax: (0227) 274655

A full list of our publications sent free on request.